# ANIMAL MAGIC

*Poems on a disappearing world*

## Liz Brownlee

Illustrations
### Rose Sanderson

IRON
PRESS

First published 2012 by IRON Press
5 Marden Terrace
Cullercoats
North Shields
NE30 4PD
tel/fax +44 (0)191 2531901
ironpress@blueyonder.co.uk
www.ironpress.co.uk

FIRST EDITION

ISBN  978-0-9565725-3-0
Printed by Fieldprint Ltd
Boldon Colliery

Typeset in  Garamond
Cover artwork & illustrations by Rose Sanderson
Book design and lay-out by
Brian Grogan & Peter Mortimer

IRON Press Books are distributed by Central Books
and represented by Inpress Books Ltd
Collingwood Buildings, 38 Collingwood Street
Newcastle on Tyne NE1 1JF
Tel: 44 (0)191 229 9555
www.inpressbooks.co.uk

# FOREWORD

LIZ BROWNLEE CAPTURES AND DISTILS THE ESSENCE OF SOME OF THE world's engaging and endangered species. Her words conjure the spirit and shape of these animals, remind us of their beauty and leave an imprint in our minds. Can we hope that most of the creatures she writes about leave behind more than just an imprint but, crucially, descendants?

Many of the species living now are in peril of extinction, not as the result of geological or astronomical cataclysms that have come close to obliterating all life in the past, but as a result of human success. The sobering truth is that the majority of species alive today will come and go without our ever knowing they were there – and they will not leave a record of their existence.

The problems we face are considerable but not especially complicated. The loss of natural habitat to fuel and feed us is a major cause of species extinction, but doing something about it may be beyond us, as it is deeply rooted in our meteoric rise from lowly ape to global conqueror. We now appropriate so much of the planet's resources for our own ends it is difficult to see how that will change.

It has been said many times before but clearly needs repeating – we are totally dependent on nature. The life support system that sustains us is made up of a large number of species – perhaps as many as 8 million – but we are familiar with much less than a quarter of them. What we can say is that they are probably all important in some way or other but as we lose more and more species year on year, we are now having to ask questions like how many species do we need to survive? Are all species equally important?  For example there are just over 200 species of owl on the planet - do we need them all and, if not, which ones can we afford to lose?

As we dash towards an ever deeper understanding of the minutiae of matter and the vastness of the cosmos, we may just have lost sight of what really matters. We are blinded by our own brilliance. As the web of life frays further and bits of the Earth's ecological machinery start to falter and then fail – what then? Will our ability to describe the interactions of subatomic particles or understand how the universe started, help us? I suspect it will not help us in the slightest. Whether there is or is not a Higgs Boson gives me scant comfort when set against the extinction, at our own hands, of countless species.

But take some comfort. The Earth is not, as some would have it, fragile – it is enduring but ever changing. Species that evolve here have a finite existence – in the case of many vertebrate species it may be anything from one to ten million years or more before they become extinct or morph into something recognisably different. The Earth will go on to produce more and more species until, in less than five billion years, it becomes a lifeless speck of space debris. On a cosmic scale life on our planet is nothing more than a flash in the darkness – like the sexual signal of a firefly, it burns brightly for a very short time.

So would it matter if orangutans became extinct and the only reminders of their existence were museum specimens and TV documentaries? Well, taking the really big picture - and you might be shocked - no it probably doesn't really matter that much. Just as the world did not end with the passing of the dinosaurs, it will not end if we lose many of the large charismatic species alive today. In time, we will regard them as curiosities as we do moas, giant tree sloths and dodos. But there is no getting away from the fact that the world will become a very much poorer place as our natural capital is cleared, felled and burned. For decades now, alarm bells have been ringing, but I can see little evidence that they are being heard. Like someone sawing away at the branch on which they sit, catastrophe, for us, seems inescapable (unless we stop sawing, of course).

Read these poems and let Liz Brownlee's words delight and charm you. Enjoy them … read them to your children. This lovely book may well last longer than some of the creatures it celebrates, so now might be a good time to draw a line in the sand. You might think it does not matter that somewhere in a dark, steamy jungle, a minute amphibian lives out its life oblivious to the changes that will overcome it – but with each lineage of creatures extinguished, our own chances of survival are diminished. It's not so much Save the Planet as Save Ourselves. This selfish imperative might have more effect than any amount of tree hugging and dolphin stroking.

The inclusion of some species in this collection of poems might seem odd. Some say city pigeons are nothing but flying rats. But they highlight the perverse way we view nature. We especially value rarity but this concept, born of commerce and materials, is not a valid measure for assessing the worth of the biosphere. As the footnotes remind us, the passenger pigeon was once so common that flying flocks numbering in the hundreds of millions would darken the skies. The passenger pigeon was killed in industrial numbers for human and pig food and for amusement. Martha, the last one, died on September 1st, 1914, at Cincinnati Zoo – a truly pathetic end for any species. But many more species, large and small, will follow the passenger pigeon in the next century. Human beings have mastered so much in such a short time, but I really wonder if we have the maturity to deal with the power we have procured. Recent advances in molecular genetics tell us that the dodo was simply a flightless pigeon and also that we are just another bipedal ape with an overgrown brain.

## Dr. George McGavin  ———————————————————
Zoologist and TV presenter

# ACKNOWLEDGEMENTS

I would like to thank the following people:

My wonderful friends, Susan Aiers, Liz Bagshaw, Kathy Hallsworth, Heather Montague and Emma Shaw, who literally first drove me to creative writing (with the excellent Crysse Morrison and Mike Johnson).

The staff at Bath Spa University MA in Writing for Young People, Nicola Davies, Julia Green, Mimi Thebo, John McLay.

The best writing group in the world, Sue Ashby, Janine Amos, Matt Bradley, Elen Caldecott, Jim Carrington, Alex Diaz, Alex Herring, Kay Leitch.

The Advancers, Sheila Glasbey, TB and all my friends who have supported and helped me.

Dorit Bar-Zakay for permission to use her wonderful photograph of red-crowned cranes as reference for Rose Sanderson's beautiful painting on the front cover.

Michael Kavanagh for his expertise on Indesign to help shape the shape poems.

Peter Brownlee, Emmelie Brownlee, Jem Brownlee.
George McGavin, Peter Mortimer.

The scientists mentioned in the notes and references – any errors or omissions are mine.

## Some of the poems were originally published as below:

Pufferfish, A Sea Creature Ate My Teacher, Ed. Brian Moses, 2000.
Bumblebee, Elephants Can't Jump, Ed. Brian Moses, Macmillan 2001.
Poison Dart Frog, Bristol Zoo, 2007.
Snow Petrels, Orangutan, Hippopotamus, Shouting at the Ocean Eds.
Graham Denton, Andrea Shavick, Roger Stevens, Hands Up Books, 2009.
Dragonfly, The Scrumbler Magazine, Ed. Michael Kavanagh, 2010.

*"... almost like they know they are on a different plane from everything else."*

I contacted species experts to ensure that the animal facts that accompany each poem are current with scientific knowledge. The scientists took time out of their busy schedules, conferences and field trips to answer my many queries with patience, humour and generosity. Their replies were vibrant with love and enthusiasm for their subjects, and were sometimes poetry themselves.

I would like to share one comment in particular about the bird that features on the front of this book:

"I can tell you that there's something different and special about the red-crowned crane that can't be explained, almost like they know they are on a different plane from everything else."

Scott Swengel
*Independent zoologist, former Curator of Birds at the International Crane Foundation.*

L.B.

**LIZ BROWNLEE** loved drawing and animals as a child. She kept rabbits, a slow worm and a mouse (unbeknown to her parents) and raised a foundling pink-skinned creature that turned out to be a Greenfinch called Grizelda, who lived to be thirteen. Liz went to art college, then film school, and worked in the advertising industry. In 1985 she moved to Bristol and started writing for children when her own were young. She has an MA in Writing for Young People from Bath Spa University, and about 60 poems in children's poetry anthologies. Liz has two children, daughter Emmelie, also a writer, and son Jem, who is at university. She lives with husband Peter (who works for the BBC Natural History Unit) and her dog and cat, Lola and Milla. www.poetlizbrownlee.co.uk

# THE CREATURES

In memory of
John and Dorothy Sidaway

With love for
Peter, Emmelie and Jem

# Pongo pygmaeus, Pongo abelii

Bornean and Sumatran orangutans are mainly arboreal. Their up–to–2m reach enables them to move by semi-brachiation, swinging through the canopy, never letting go of one branch until the next is grasped.

Adult male Orangutans weigh 50–90kg, females 30–50kg – they are the heaviest primates to live in trees, and a fall could cause them serious injury or death. Museum skeletons show evidence of many incidences of healed fractures in big primates. These injuries are thought to happen mainly when they are young. So they are cautious climbers; if unsure, they test branches carefully before trusting their full weight on them.

According to the World Wildlife Fund, released orangutans have been observed using tools for many purposes, such as digging and fighting. They have even been seen untying the complex knots that secure boats and rafts, shoving off, boarding, and riding across rivers.

RANGE: Rainforests in Borneo and Sumatra in South Eastern Asia.

DIET: 60% fruit, with smaller amounts of young leaves and shoots, bark, woody lianas, insects and soil.

SIZE: Male orangutans grow up to 1.5m, females up to 1.2m.

STATUS: The IUCN Red List of Threatened Species has classified Bornean orangutans as Endangered and Sumatran orangutans as Critically Endangered. 80% of the forests in which they live have been cut down in the last twenty years. Scientists think they may be extinct within ten years, unless deforestation can be halted.

# Orangutan

A heavy hulk and tum like mine,
in shades of hairy clementine,
means when I'm up my forest tree,
I live my whole life – gingerly!

# Lithobates sylvaticus

Alaskan wood frogs have the amazing ability to freeze for three months during the winter, and come to no harm. As the weather becomes colder, they burrow under mosses and leaves. Their livers start to convert glycogen to glucose and flood their tissues with it. This protects the water inside their cells from freezing, and even though ice forms between them, it stops the delicate cell walls from being broken.

Insulated by snow, they can survive their body temperature dropping to −18C, while the outside air temperature can drop to −50C. In spring they thaw, their hearts start beating again, and they hop to nearby ponds to mate.

RANGE: Wood frogs live relatively widely in northern North America and further north than any other frog in Alaska.

DIET: Small invertebrates.

SIZE: 3.4–7.8cm nose to tail.

STATUS: Wood frogs are not endangered, but need several types of habitat that are connected. These are rapidly vanishing. Further south in the United States, wood frogs' wetlands are not protected – in Wyoming they are listed as a species of potential concern, and in Arkansas as a species of special concern.

Alaskan wood frogs are falling prey to increasing numbers of deformities, from about 2% up to 20% in one area. As frogs breathe through their skins, they are sensitive to toxins, and can give early warning of environmental problems. Scientists are investigating if these deformities are due to agricultural chemicals, chemical contaminants, parasites or exposure to UVB radiation.

# Alaskan Wood Frog

As snow falls slowly,
frond by frond,
and turns opaque
the snowmelt pond,

this small green wood frog
starts to freeze,
his hands and feet,
elbows and knees.

His eyes and brain
and blood are chilled,
his steams of breath
and heart are stilled.

As frog turns ice
it's hard to know,
what is the frog,
and what is snow.

Yet when the snow
ponds melt, they bring
this little frog
awake to spring.

# *Uroplatus henkeli*

Henkel's leaf-tailed geckos have markings so extraordinarily like the bark of the trees in which they live, they are virtually invisible unless they move. When they lie on the bark, generally head downward, a flap of skin around the edge of their bodies breaks up their outline. This makes them even more indistinguishable. A leaf-like tail adds to their camouflage. Large adhesive toe-pads on their feet enable them to climb extremely well.

RANGE: Rain forest and dry forest in the north and west of Madagascar.

DIET: Insects.

SIZE: Individuals from western Madagascar can reach up to 30cm, making them among the largest geckos in the world.

STATUS: These geckos are classified Vulnerable on the IUCN Red List, as their forest is threatened by ongoing logging and expanding agriculture.

# Leaf-Tailed Gecko

Moth-flat,
flecks and speckles
so exact
all along it,

as if the
mosses that
it's on
lie upon it,

the branch's
echo –
a leaf-tailed
gecko

# Nephila komachi

These golden orb-weaving spiders, only discovered in 2009, are the largest ever found. The huge female spiders weave a web often over 90cm wide, made of golden silk, which reflects light in a way that attracts insects.

Orb spiders have hairy legs that are very sensitive to vibrations. They sit with their legs touching their web. When an insect gets caught in their sticky silk, the spiders can tell how far away and which direction it is in.

RANGE: Forest in Madagascar and Maputaland.

DIET: Insects.

SIZE: Females 10–13cm, males only 3cm.

STATUS: These spiders have not been assessed by the IUCN Red List, but are very rare. At one time they were feared extinct. Only one specimen was found in a museum in South Africa, in 2000, and searches in the wild failed to find a live one. Then a second specimen was found in a museum in Austria, and finally three live spiders were found in Tembe Elephant Park, South Africa. None have been found since. Their only habitats are in two endangered biodiversity hotspots.

# Orb Spider

I touch my silk

and listen to its

faint taut song –

until the cords are

broken when dinner

comes along.

# Amblyornis inornatus

Vogelkop bowerbirds make and decorate their impressive, architecturally masterful bowers to impress females. They use a much more diverse and vivid set of colours in their decorations than most other bowerbirds, and are especially fond of anything rare or unusual. They will even use brightly-coloured plastic items.

They are good singers and can mimic many of the birdsongs in their forest.

RANGE: A small mountain area on the Vogelkop peninsula in New Guinea, Indonesia.

DIET: Fruit, flowers, insects and nectar.

SIZE: 25cm long.

STATUS: Vogelkop bowerbirds have not been assessed by the IUCN Red List. Roads being built into their habitat are the biggest threat to these birds.

Although New Guinea is home to the largest pristine rainforest in the Asia-Pacific, the World Wildlife Fund warns that a destructive patchwork of logging concessions, oil palm plantations, mines and roads are planned. This could see the island lose a third of its remaining rainforest.

# Vogelkop Bowerbird

Before his bower,
a pyramid
of orchid stems
supported by pillars,

appointed by
plum berries and blue,
(plucked with
delicate precision)

and displayed
precisely beside
sprays of pink
blossom,

a shiny pile
of purple-grey
beetle wings,
and one perfect

crimson petal,
the plainest
bowerbird
proudly places


himself.

# Anguilla anguilla

European eels lay their eggs in the Sargasso Sea in the North Atlantic. They hatch into leaf-shaped, transparent and almost invisible leptocephali, so unlike their parents, scientists didn't realise they were baby eel larvae until recently.

Leptocephali drift with the Gulf Stream for up to three years. By the time they have changed into elvers they have reached the mouths of European rivers, which they swim up, still growing, until they are full sized eels. Then they mate and swim back to the Sargasso Sea to lay their eggs and die.

RANGE: North Atlantic.

DIET: Marine snow, tiny particles of food stirred up by ocean eddies, until they change into fish-eating elvers and eels.

SIZE: Leptocephali 6cm, elvers 7–10cm, eels 60–70cm.

STATUS: European eels are regionally classified by the IUCN Red List as Critically Endangered. Eels worldwide are endangered.

The WWF states that European eels have several life history characteristics which make them particularly vulnerable to overexploitation: they are long-lived, have a large body size, a late sexual maturity, produce all their offspring at one time, have high mortality rates, and a trans-Atlantic migration route. Poaching and illegal trade are a concern for this species. Declines may be further exacerbated by other factors such as freshwater and coastal habitat loss, pollution, parasitism, climate change, ocean current change, and blocking of inland migration routes.

# Baby Eels

Baby eels,
I don't know why,
are called
lep-to-ceph-ali.

And head to fin
they are so thin,
you see the sea through
their see-through skin.

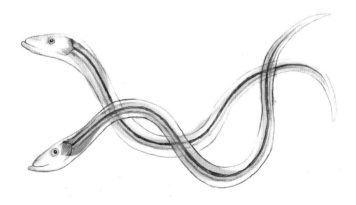

# Panthera uncia

Snow leopards are shy, elusive and solitary – an attack on human beings has never been recorded. Their almost-white coats are marked with black rosettes right along their body to their long, thick tails, which they use to balance and curl round them to keep warm while sleeping.

They can leap as far as 15m, further than any other cat.

RANGE: High mountain ranges of central Asia and southern Asia, although they are now extinct in some areas. They prefer high, steep, rocky terrain in the alpine zone in the summer, where plants like rhododendrons and mountain roses grow, and the sub-alpine zone in the winter.

DIET: Mainly bharal (blue sheep) and wild goats called ibex. Because their natural prey are becoming fewer, in some places domestic animals such as sheep, goats, horses and yak can make up to 58% of their diet.

SIZE: 60cm high at the shoulder, with a 1.3m head and body, and a 1m tail.

STATUS: Snow leopards are classified as Endangered on the IUCN Red List. Major threats to them include loss of their prey due to illegal hunting and competition with farm animals. Problems also include a lack of conservation capacity, policy and awareness. The World Wildlife Fund states that many snow leopards are killed by farmers wishing to protect their farm animals, and for their coveted fur and bones, which are used in Chinese medicines.

# Snow Leopard

The white
swirling air
spins a
leopard
who walks
quietly
the lines
on the face
of the mountain.

A snow coat,
with shadow roses
flows sheer
as water
finds its way,

soft as snow
falling
on snow,

becoming
snow again.

# Rhacophorus reinwardtii

Reinwardt's or green flying frogs have large hands and feet with areas of purple to black webbed skin between each finger and toe. When they jump from a branch they spread their fingers and toes to open up all of their webbed hands and feet to the air. Then they glide like a piece of paper to another tree, where they use their big toes to sucker themselves a soft, safe landing.

RANGE: Southern Thailand, Malaysia, and Indonesia in rainforests, mainly at lower altitudes but up to 1,400m above sea level. Almost entirely arboreal after their tadpole stage, they live in the upper canopy of the trees, only coming down to mate and lay eggs.

DIET: Insects and other small invertebrates.

SIZE: 7–12cm in length.

STATUS: These frogs are decreasing in numbers and are classified by the IUCN Red List as Near Threatened, the main threat to them being the loss of their rainforest habitat. Removal of mature lowland forest through logging, agricultural expansion and human settlements has reduced the available habitat significantly for this species.

Of the 76 frogs in the same genus listed by the IUCN Red List, 29 more are classified from Near Threatened to Critically Endangered, mainly due to loss of habitat.

# Flying Frog

Where the green hands of the forest
  hold a fierce and humid heat,
    a gorgeous, gleaming frog
  leaps from his leaf-high seat.

He doesn't fall, he stretches out,
  and glides his tree-top routes,
    for all his toes and fingers
  come equipped with parachutes.

# Crotalus unicolour

Aruba Island rattlesnakes are only found on Aruba. These small snakes are pinkish-brown with pale blue, brown and pink diamond markings.

Rattlesnakes are shy creatures that do not attack unless cornered and unable to escape – they usually advertise their presence and warn predators by rattling the end of their tail. Many rattlesnakes are killed needlessly – they are an important part of ecosystems, keeping populations of rats and other vermin under control.

They have two pits either side of their head that can detect the heat of their prey. Scientists at California Academy of Sciences in San Francisco have proven that rattlesnakes can bite for up to an hour after death, a reflex possibly triggered by their infrared sensor pits.

Rattlesnake bites are seldom inflicted, and hardly ever fatal if treated.

RANGE: The Caribbean island of Aruba.

DIET: Thought to be small rabbits, lizards and possibly rodents.

SIZE: Less than 1m long.

STATUS: These snakes are classified Critically Endangered by the IUCN Red List. With an estimated number of only 250 remaining by some authorities, they are one of the rarest rattlesnakes in the world. Their habitat used to be densely wooded, but most trees have been cut down, and their land is used for grazing by sheep, goats and donkeys. Introduced boa constrictors are also competing for food.

# Rattlesnake

A
simple
creature,
mainly
spine,
ribs,
skull,
diamond
skin
curving
straight
paths,
it can
sense
the heat
of a
small
heart
beating
and
gather
taste
even
before
its
fangs
unfold,
bite -
and the
small
heart
stops.
Listen
to its
rattle
warning.
Keep well
clear.

It will
only
strike
in fear.

# Columba livia

Egyptian hieroglyphics show that pigeons have lived with humans for at least 5,000 years. City pigeons are descendants of escaped domesticated rock pigeons. Selective breeding changed them from their original 'blue bar' (dark and light greys, some iridescence and black bars on wings and tail) into many more colours. They still strut in soft browns, russet, whites, checkers and other combinations in all our cities. This interests scientists as most animals that escape captivity revert to their wild colours within a few generations.

RANGE: All over the world in every city.

DIET: Seeds, grains, fruit and human leftovers.

SIZE: Female pigeons 29–35cm, males 30–36cm.

STATUS: City pigeons are not endangered, even by wood pigeons moving in to their city territories. But there are twelve in the same genus classified on the IUCN Red List, from Near Threatened to Critically Endangered.

One type of pigeon that numbered billions suffered one of the biggest extinctions of all time. When North American settlers first encountered the passenger pigeon, there were so many of them that in flight they made the sky dark and a flock could take days to pass overhead. When the settlers cleared forests for agriculture, the pigeons began to eat the farmers' grain and were treated as vermin, killed for sport and used as food.

The last passenger pigeon died in Cincinnati Zoo in 1914. One valuable outcome of this was an arousal of public interest in the need for strong conservation laws in North America.

do city pigeons
         on cold, grey ledges
                  give a high coo?

# Ophiacantha spectabilis

This unnamed brittle star is a type of sea star (formerly known as starfish). All sea stars are hollow, with sensitive skin inside and outside. Seawater flows into as well as surrounding them. They feel sea in every direction and so are very aware of any change in their surroundings. Many types of sea star live in shallow and deep-sea water all over the world, in every habitat and even on each other.

RANGE: In coral species *Solenosmilia* on seamounts (undersea mountains) off Australia and in the North Atlantic.

DIET: They are carnivorous.

SIZE: Central disc about 9mm, arm tip to arm tip about 8cm.

STATUS: Seamounts are crucial ecosystems, causing currents that carry nutrition up from the deep sea floor. This supports many species, such as corals and animals living on them, and those visiting the mount, like sea turtles. Trawlers and fishing nets easily damage corals on seamounts, making the many animals living on them vulnerable. Corals do not grow very fast and reproduce/settle infrequently, so recovery is very slow (maybe hundreds to thousands of years).

Sea star species are adapted to particular temperatures of water, making them vulnerable to climate change. As their structures are higher in magnesium than other creatures, sea stars and other echinoderms are also vulnerable to acidification of the seas.

Some scientists think acidification of the sea by carbon dioxide absorption is the greatest threat to all living creatures.

# Sea Star

she wanders in a ceaseless, starless night.

Deep undersea, a sea star sighs, no brain,

no blood, no beating heart, no eyes

no breeze, no changing skies, no light,

sea in her soul, its stroke her sight, no moon,

# Typophyllum lunatum

These leaf-mimic insects are bush crickets. They have bodies and wings (each unique) with the colourings, textures, and markings of leaves – some even have holes as if a caterpillar has nibbled them. This makes them look as much like leaves and as little like insects as possible. They stay still, except to sway in the breeze, during the day. Then, when darkness falls, and all the birds that might eat them are asleep, they become walking leaves and eat the real leaves round them.

Insects related to today's bush crickets, showing leaf mimicking, have been found in fossils in France and England. They have successfully used this way of disguising themselves from predators for 35 million years.

RANGE: Peru in the Amazon rainforest.

DIET: Leaves.

SIZE: 5–10cm.

STATUS: These particular leaf-mimic insects are fantastically disguised to avoid the threats they face. However, no matter how wonderfully they have adapted to survive, they cannot hope to escape the loss of habitat they face each year as 150,000 hectares of the Peruvian forest they live in are cut down.

# Leaf-Mimic Insect

She hides sunlit
and in plain view,
as if she had
unfurled and grew,

so like the leaves
hung in the trees,
her green wings flutter
in the breeze,

until at dark
without a qualm,
she eats what kept her
safe from harm.

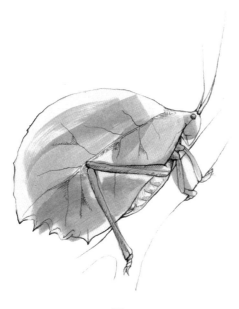

# Oophaga arborea

Female polkadot poison frogs lay eggs on bromeliads in the canopy of cloud forests. When they hatch their tadpoles live in the pools of water caught in the curls of leaves. The mother frogs periodically lay infertile eggs in the pools for each tadpole to eat while it develops into a frog.

These frogs were only discovered recently, when trees were felled to make way for a road.

RANGE: Endemic to the Western Cordilleras and Atlantic lowlands of Panama. They occur higher than other poison frogs, up to at least 1,120m.

DIET: Ants and small insects.

SIZE: 2.0–2.2cm.

STATUS: These frogs are classified as Endangered by the IUCN Red List. They are threatened by habitat loss due to logging, livestock ranching and human settlement, and are potentially at risk from the chytridiomycosis fungus, a fungus that is spreading across the world, wiping out many species of amphibian.

Of the other eight members in the *Oophaga* genus assessed by the IUCN Red List, four more are classified as Near Threatened, Vulnerable, Endangered and Critically Endangered. Causes include logging, human settlement, and collection for the pet trade.

# Polkadot Frog

In green-bright
bromeliads
cloud mountain high,

reaching from
branches to blue
topaz sky,

where mosses
breathe mists,
and flame flowers drip,

and amethyst
hummingbirds
hover to sip,

the curl of a leaf
swirled by
sheltering fog,

holds a
miniature tadpole,
and polkadot frog.

# Hippopotamus amphibius

Hippopotamuses are considered to be the most dangerous animal living in Africa, killing more humans than all the other animals combined. Charging hippopotamuses can run at 30km/h. Weighing up to 3,200kg, with 5cm thick skin over a deep layer of fat, they are the third heaviest terrestrial animal after the elephant and white rhino. It's best not to get between them and where they want to go.

Adult hippos are graceful in water, and can hold their breath for five minutes, but their bodies are too dense to float or swim. Their specific gravity (density compared to water) allows them to sink and stand on, bounce off or run along the river bottom.

They spend most of the day in the cooling water and emerge to feed at night.

RANGE: Rivers, lakes and swampy areas throughout sub-Saharan Africa.

DIET: Grasses, and sometimes fallen fruit.

SIZE: Males are up to 1.65m high and 5m long. Females smaller, up to 1.45m high. A large male's mouth can open up to a cavernous 1.25m.

STATUS: Once common, hippos are now classified as Vulnerable by the IUCN Red List, due to illegal and unregulated hunting for meat and ivory (found in their canine teeth) and habitat loss.

# Hippopotamus

A hippo's round rubbery form,
is bursting with blubbery brawn,
with his mouth open wide
he could fit you inside,
thank goodness he only eats lawn!

## Corytophanes crystatus

Helmeted iguanas are extremely well camouflaged in greens and browns, and sit absolutely motionless on leaves or branches, waiting for an insect to land or crawl nearby.

On a few occasions, scientists have found small algae growing on their skin, which would make them even more cryptic. Apparently the algae grows without affecting them, possibly because the plants are shed periodically with their skin, before they can damage their health.

RANGE: Forests from Central Velacruz, Mexico, down through the west margin of the Yucatan peninsular, to Costa Rica, Panama and Colombia.

DIET: Large arthropods including katydids, beetles and spiders.

SIZE: They can grow up to 36cm from snout to the end of their tails.

STATUS: Helmeted iguanas have not been assessed yet by the IUCN Red List. However, all the rainforests in which they live are endangered and suffering extensive deforestation, and one is on the United Nations Educational, Scientific and Cultural Organisation (UNESCO)'s List of World Heritage in Danger. In addition to this, their population densities are thought to be low.

# Iguana

He crouched and
waited patiently,
in green on
green he hid,

then switched from
still to swiftly kill
a careless
katydid.

When katydid was
done and gone,
quiet hours in
sun and rain,

helped lichen grow
upon his head,
as he waited,
still, again.

# Colias croceus

Some clouded yellow butterflies are seen every year. Occasionally they come in huge numbers and these are known to butterfly enthusiasts as 'clouded yellow years'.

RANGE: Breeding range, North Africa and Southern Europe, eastwards through Turkey and the Middle East, Asia except Central Asia. Increasingly a summer visitor further north into North Europe, occasionally as far as Scandinavia.

DIET: Caterpillars feed on clover and birds-foot trefoil.

SIZE: 5.2–6.2cm.

STATUS: Clouded yellow butterflies are not endangered; they are migratory and common summer visitors to Great Britain. However they are over-wintering more frequently due to warmer winters. If climate change continues more insect species may find permanent homes further north, possibly competing with our resident species. Less welcome insects than the clouded yellow butterfly would be those considered pests, such as mosquitoes.

Butterfly Conservation states that 76% of our resident butterfly species in Great Britain have declined since the 1970s, and 31% are classified as threatened with Extinction on the Red List for British butterflies. This is mainly due to intensive farming methods and habitat loss.

a yellow leaf
falls skywards –
autumn butterfly

# Grus japonensis

In Japan, red-crowned cranes are held sacred as symbols of loyalty, long life and love, because they pair for life. They reinforce their partnerships by dancing before they mate. But they dance at other times too, such as after bathing, when the weather is warm and balmy and also at midnight even in the coldest days of winter. They appear to enjoy dancing and if one individual or pair starts to dance, others join in.

RANGE: Japanese red-crowned cranes live on the island of Hokkaido in Northern Japan. However there is also a migratory population that breeds in China and migrates to North Eastern China, Mongolia, Korea and Russia for the winter.

DIET: Whatever is available, including reeds, grasses, fish, insects, and rodents.

SIZE: 1.5m high.

STATUS: Red-crowned cranes are classified by the IUCN Red List as Endangered and number only around 2,750 in total. Numbers are decreasing and threats include fire, loss of breeding grounds due to lowering of water levels, new agriculture and industry and, in some areas, poisoning by pollution.

# Red-Crowned Cranes

Two red-crowned
cranes dance,

a ritual,
graceful,

light as
threadbare silk

lifting on
invisible clouds

over which
to drape

their swooping
necks in one

curving heart.

# Felis margarita

Sand cats are secretive and rarely seen, spending the daytime out of the heat, dug deep in their burrows. They bury their scats and have fur-covered, sand-gripping feet that do not leave tracks, and that insulate them from extremes of temperature.

They can apparently live without drinking at all, obtaining their water from the juices of their prey, although they will drink water if it is available.

RANGE: Deserts in Africa and Asia.

DIET: Hunting at night, they use their huge ears to listen for small burrowing mammals such as jerboas under the sand. Also birds, insects and reptiles.

SIZE: 26cm high, 40cm long, with a 25cm tail – about the same size as a domestic cat.

STATUS: Sand cats are classified by the IUCN Red List as Near Threatened. Habitat degradation is a major threat, as is the fluctuation of their food supply due to drought. Feral dogs and cats that compete for food and carry disease also affect them. Some are caught in traps laid for other animals.

# Sand Cat

Quiet furred feet
leave no prints
where he stands,

coat the same shade
as his yellow-
grained land,

hiding
from prey like a
cat made of sand.

# *Odorrana tormota*

Torrent frogs' bird-like, melodic chirps are barely audible above the very noisy environment in which they live, so they have developed the unusual ability to call and hear partly in ultrasound. They are one of only two frogs known to have this ability.

Unlike other frogs (but like mammals), they possess ear canals, with eardrums situated at the end of the canals. Their eardrums are very thin, enabling them to vibrate easily at such a high frequency and transmit ultrasonic vibrations to the inner ear.

Being able to hear and use different frequencies to the sounds of the stream means other torrent frogs can clearly hear their calls, whilst they remain unheard by predators. This gives the male and female the ability to find each other very accurately.

RANGE: In bushes at the edge of rushing streams, in the Huangshan and Zhejiang Provinces of Central China.

DIET: Insects and other invertebrates.

SIZE: 3.2–5.6cm.

STATUS: Torrent frogs' populations are decreasing, and they are classified as Vulnerable by the IUCN Red List. The main threat to these frogs is habitat loss due to agriculture and clear-cutting (the felling and removal of all trees from a forest area).

# Torrent Frog

Beside the rush
of waterfalling,
the torrent frog
is calling, calling

to the torrent
frogs surrounding,
through the waters
pounding, pounding,

over birdsong,
insect drones,
hard rain pelting,
pelting stones,

the torrent frogs
can hear through all,
though silent, silent
is their call.

# Alauda arvensis

Skylarks, in their unassuming brown plumage, blend invisibly into vegetation on the ground.

In their breeding season, between April and August, male skylarks are famous for their territorial displays. They ascend almost vertically high into the sky, and sing a stream of song that seems to celebrate summer.

RANGE: All over Europe, in some parts of Asia and as far east as Japan. Skylarks like open ground, with vegetation that isn't too high.

DIET: Seeds and insects.

SIZE: 16cm long.

STATUS: Skylarks are on the RSPB Red List of 'Birds of Conservation Concern' and are a UK Biodiversity Action Plan (UK BAP) priority bird species.

Changes in farming practice, where crops are no longer planted in spring but in autumn, mean that by summer, crops are already too dense for skylarks to run through to find their food. This is one of the reasons for their widespread disappearance.

Skylarks survive in Great Britain only because of the RSPB's reserves.

song


my
spill
and
sky
the
touch
I
until
ascent
vertical
a
on
joy
my
take
I

# Skylark

# Chrysina strasseni

There are many types of shiny mirror beetle in shades of silver, gold, green and rose.

Scientists have discovered that mirror beetles' wing cases, made of a substance similar to our nails, are structured in layers. The layers become thinner towards the inside. This cuticle reflects every colour of light back to the eye, but directionally, concentrated into a specular reflection like that of light off a polished surface.

It is suggested that this ability enables the beetles to shine like drops of water and hide in a rainforest of reflections. Another theory is that their mirror-like carapace echoes the colour of their surroundings as camouflage.

RANGE: Forests in Honduras, Central America.

DIET: Vegetation.

SIZE: 2.5cm.

STATUS: As with most insects, the IUCN Red List has not yet assessed mirror beetles. However, Honduras is one of the world's poorest countries and its forests are not well protected, being cut down for fuel, timber, mining and agriculture at a rate of over 102,000 hectares a year. Honduran mahogany has already been depleted to exhaustion.

Honduran rainforests are on the United Nations Educational, Scientific and Cultural Organisation (UNESCO)'s List of World Heritage in Danger.

# Mirror Beetle

I am the colour
of all that I see,
the leaves changing colour
also change me,

and so when I rest
and then when I fly,
I am the branches,
I am the sky.

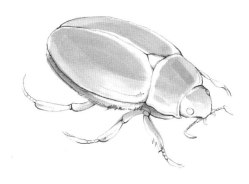

# Crocodylus mindorensis

Philippine crocodiles have dark markings running down their bodies and stripes along their tails. They are relatively unstudied. Saltwater crocodiles, some of the largest crocodiles in the world, also live around these islands. Contact with these aggressive crocodiles in the past has been a reason for local inhabitants' intolerance and fear of the freshwater ones.

Crocodiles and their ancestors have been on earth 80 million years. In this time, continents have drifted apart, mountains formed, rivers changed course countless times, dinosaurs come and gone, and man appeared. Crocodiles have remained relatively unchanged, and a successful species until recently.

RANGE: Freshwater marshes, tributaries of large rivers and small lakes and ponds on a few Philippine islands.

DIET: Thought to eat fish, invertebrates, small reptiles and amphibians.

SIZE: Up to 3m long.

STATUS: Philippine crocodiles are classified as Critically Endangered by the IUCN Red List. There are thought to be fewer than 100 adults in the wild. Habitat destruction is the major cause of decline in both species of crocodile in the Philippines. There is a captive breeding scheme and a program is now in place to establish protected areas to release Philippine crocodiles back into the wild.

Of the 23 species of crocodilians, five are currently listed as Critically Endangered, two as Endangered.

# Crocodile

Crocodile.

Perfectly
suspended,

only nostrils
and eyes

above the
waterline,
waiting.

A long
observance.

Older than
the trees,

older than
the river's

journey.

# Phyllobates terribilis

Golden poison dart frogs are among the most poisonous creatures in the world. It is possible to die simply from touching them. One frog contains enough poison to kill several humans.

It is not known how they produce batrachotoxin, the poison in their skin, but it is thought it might be a mixture of chemicals brought together from their diet.

These frogs came by their name as their skins used to be heated by natives to drip poison onto darts to blow at their prey. Darts treated in this way could still kill months later.

RANGE: Found only in tiny areas on the Pacific coast of Colombia, occurring up to 200m above sea level.

DIET: Arthropods, including ants, and possibly some plants.

SIZE: Up to 5.5cm.

STATUS: These frogs are classified by the IUCN Red List as Endangered. The major threats to them are deforestation for agricultural development, the illegal planting of crops, logging, human settlement and pollution resulting from the spraying of illegal crops. They are occasionally reported as being sold for the pet trade.

# Poison Dart Frog

Oh, little gold frog,
so shiny and smart,
each of your jumps
is a gold poison dart!

# *Morus capensis*

Cape gannets have yellow heads, pale blue bills and black-dipped wings. Diving gannets hit the sea at speeds reaching 100km/h. To prevent broken bones, they have air sacs like bubble wrap in their faces. Acting like air bags in a car, they absorb the shock and soften the blow when the birds hit the water.

RANGE: They only breed at six islands, Bird (Lambert's Bay), Bird (Algoa Bay) and Malgas in South Africa, and Mercury, Ichaboe and Possession in Namibia.

DIET: Mainly anchovies, sardines, saury and offal discarded by fishing boats.

SIZE: 80–94cm long.

STATUS: These gannets are listed as Vulnerable by the IUCN Red List. This is due to their very small breeding range and over-exploitation of their prey by human fisheries, compounded by pollution, causing a continuous decline in the quality of surrounding waters for foraging.

Dr. René Navarro (Zoology Dept. at the University of Cape Town) reports that an important factor that significantly reduces their breeding success is predation. Problems include kelp gulls, cape fur seals (as many as 40% of their chicks are taken by these seals at Malgas Island) and great white pelicans that can swallow chicks in one gulp.

Birdlife South Africa and WWF South Africa have reported that Cape gannets are also seriously affected by long-line fishing along the coast of West Africa, Namibia and Angola.

# Gannet

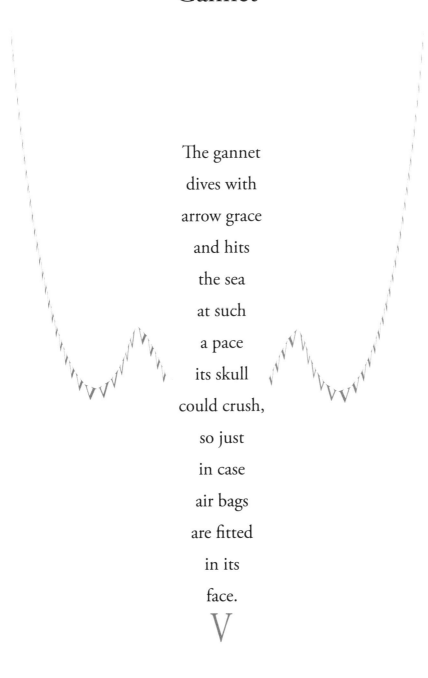

The gannet

dives with

arrow grace

and hits

the sea

at such

a pace

its skull

could crush,

so just

in case

air bags

are fitted

in its

face.

V

# Suncus fellowesgordoni

Not a lot is known about these little chocolate or Sri-Lankan pygmy shrews, as they have not been studied much.

However, because of their size, like all pygmy shrews, they must have to search constantly for food, and eat approximately every two hours. As they search, they squeak.

Their close relatives, the slightly smaller European pygmy shrews, are by mass the smallest mammals in the world, so small they sometimes sleep in beetle burrows.

RANGE: The central highlands of Sri Lanka, in mountain forests.

DIET: They are insectivores.

SIZE:  8.5cm nose to tail.

STATUS: Chocolate pygmy shrews are classified as Endangered by the IUCN Red List, because of the continuing decline of their forest habitat, due to fire and conversion to plantations of cardamom and tea.

# Pygmy Shrew

A pygmy shrew
is minuscule
and very
hard to seek,

for it's true
the pygmy shrew's
just whiskers,
nose and squeak.

# Branta ruficollis

Red-breasted geese are the smallest and one of the rarest types of geese, feathered in chestnut, black and white.

Geese often fly in a 'V' formation, as each goose feels the help of lift generated by the air disturbed by the goose in front. Studies on geese have shown that they gain an energy saving of about 10% by flying like this. When the lead goose gets tired, another one takes over.

RANGE: Breeding in Russia and wintering mainly in Bulgaria and Romania, with smaller numbers congregating in the Ukraine and, in severe winters, Greece.

DIET: In the summer breeding grounds they eat grass, leaves and shoots; in the winter they eat grains and grasses.

SIZE: 53–55cm long.

STATUS: These geese are classified Endangered on the IUCN Red List. Land privatisation in their winter-feeding areas, changes in agricultural practices and loss of feeding areas in Bulgaria are major threats. They are hunted by tourists in the Ukraine and shot at staging posts in Russia. There is also pressure to allow shooting and scaring them away in Bulgaria and Romania. Climate change is expected to impact badly upon them.

# Geese

On watersilk sky
geese point
the way
a

On watersilk sky
geese point
the way

goose behind
each wing
moving
in

goose behind
each wing
moving

the lee of
another
each
as

the lee of
another
each

high as clouds
parting

high as clouds
parting
thin
air

thin

laughing
as they

laughing
as they
fly

# Mrymica sabuleti

These red ants are parasitised by one of the world's most threatened species of butterflies. Large blue butterfly caterpillars secrete chemicals that mimic the smell of the ants' own grubs – the ants are attracted and fooled into taking the caterpillars back to their nests. There the caterpillars feed on ant grubs for ten months before pupating and emerging as butterflies.

RANGE: In the soil, also in decayed wood in grass, particularly well-grazed fields and pastureland.

DIET: Small insects and honeydew.

SIZE: 4–5mm

STATUS: These ants and butterflies were affected by changes in farming practice and a fall in rabbit populations. This meant grass grew slightly longer, which caused the soil temperature to drop, so the ants could not survive. Without the ants, neither could the butterflies, and in 1979 they became extinct in Great Britain.

Professor Jeremy Thomas (Dept. of Zoology, University of Oxford) studied the reasons for the butterflies' decline. This led to them being reintroduced into Great Britain successfully, thanks to schemes where the correct turf length is provided over a large enough area to support the ants and the butterflies. The decline of these two species was affected by a change of as little as 1cm in grass length.

*Myrmica sabuleti* ants are themselves parasitised by *Myrmica hirsuta* (hairy red) ants, a species that is classified Vulnerable by the IUCN Red List in the UK.

ants' nest...

even the gaps
move

## Elaphe taeniura

Malaysian cave racer snakes are pale yellowy-white, much lighter than other brown-patterned cave racers. They are one of the least-studied snakes in South East Asia. They can climb cave walls, and they rest there on ledges or coil themselves around stalactites, with their heads hanging out ready to intercept prey.

RANGE: They live in one of a few Malaysian caves their entire lives. The other ten types of these specialised cave snakes live in tropical caves and also forests in China, down through Malaysia to Indonesia and Borneo.

DIET: Small birds called cave swiftlets and bats.

SIZE: 2.5m

STATUS: These snakes have not been assessed by the IUCN Red List, but only live in the few caves in Malaysia that also house bats. The maximum number seen in any one cave is only four. They are very rare, have no protection in Malaysia, and there is evidence that they are being collected from the wild. The limestone caves they live in are also under threat, as they are a source of marble and cement.

# Cave Racer Snake

In the darkness,
pale as light,

coiled around a
stalactite,

mouth wide open
poised to bite,

she takes him from
the air in flight,

and air from him
by squeezing tight -

cave racer snake
eats bat tonight.

# Muscardinus avellanarius

Dormice are mostly nocturnal and arboreal. Living up to five years, longer than any other mouse, their bushy tail is also unique.

In the summer they make a resting nest. These are off the ground, in a hollow tree, an old squirrel dray or bird's nest, or woven by themselves. In a cool summer they sometimes rest there in a condition of torpor, their temperature dropping to little more than their surroundings. This economises on energy, and helps if food is scarce.

In winter they hibernate for six months, usually on the ground in a damp place, to keep cool and to avoid dehydration. This nest is tightly woven from strips of honeysuckle bark, grass, and moss, sometimes with feathers or wool added for a duvet.

RANGE: Most of Europe.

DIET: Nuts, in which they nibble neat, round holes which are smoother than those nibbled by other small rodents, as well as flowers, fruit and some insects.

SIZE: 8.5cm from nose to tail.

STATUS: Dormice are listed on the UK Biodiversity Action Plan (UK BAP) as a priority terrestrial species and are one of Great Britain's most endangered mammals. They have become extinct in six counties and their numbers have dropped by 50% in the last 100 years. Their populations are still declining due to loss of hedgerows and trees and competition from grey squirrels. Dormice are important, as their presence is an indication of habitat integrity and sustainable populations of other sensitive species.

# Dormouse

With whiskers trembling, pattering feet,
round nose sniffing round berries to eat,
his round black eyes as black as coals,
nibbling in nut-shells neat round holes,

or in his woven round grass bed,
tail curling round his nose and head,
the hazel dormouse can be found,
sleeping half the year right round.

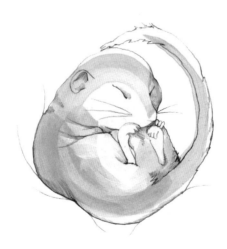

# *Afrixalus delicates*

Origami frogs are also called Pickersgill's banana frogs. The males and females work together during mating to fold leaves with their feet, to hold their eggs as they are laid. They stick the edges of the leaves together with secretions from the female's oviduct. The eggs stay unseen and safe until they hatch, at which time the tadpoles are heavy enough to slide out of the nest, down the leaves, and into the water over which the leaves are growing.

RANGE: Marere in Somalia, downwards through south eastern Africa to Avoca and Mount Edgecombe in KwaZulu-Natal (eastern South Africa), in long-leaved plants beside marshes and pools of water.

DIET: Insects.

SIZE: 2.4cm

STATUS: According to the IUCN Red List, origami frogs are not endangered, but their population is decreasing, and they are threatened in the south of their range by sugar cane farming, urbanisation and the spread of eucalyptus. This dries up the wetlands they rely on; wetlands are traditionally viewed as wastelands and not protected.

Twelve of their genus are classified by the IUCN Red List as Near Threatened, Vulnerable or Endangered, mainly due to loss of habitat.

# Origami Frog

When rain is warm
and air is balmy,

the frog who uses
origami,

holds his mate
close to his chest,

folds reed leaves
to make a nest,

and while frog love
is slowly made,

their eggs are in
the cradle laid.

# *Troglodytes cobbi*

Cobb's wrens or rock wrens are chestnut red, with dark bills and eyes and the distinctive small, round wren form with upturned tail.

These wrens are fairly unafraid of human presence. They spend most of their time on the ground, hopping from boulder to boulder to find food. They disappear and hide among the rocks rather than fly from threats.

They make round nests of grasses on the ground, hidden in a type of tussock grass stems or rock crevices, lined with feathers.

RANGE:  Only around the coast of the Falkland Islands.

DIET:  Invertebrates in seaweed and under stones. Also seeds.

SIZE: 12cm long.

STATUS: Cobb's wrens are classified as Vulnerable by the IUCN Red List. It is thought that rats, accidentally introduced to the Falkland Islands, are preying on their eggs and young.

# Wren

Red-brown wren,
how loud you sing
for such a dainty
little thing,

trembling
head to foot along,
tip-tail to beak,
you are your song.

# Bombus sylvarum

Shrill carder bumblebees fly quickly and nimbly through tall grasses at the level of the flowers beneath. Their buzz is higher pitched than normal.

Applying the principles of fixed wing aerodynamics, a zoologist once said bees are too heavy and the wrong shape to fly. Experiments by Professor Ismet Gursal (Dept. of Mechanical Engineering, University of Bath) have only recently shown exactly how they do fly. They beat their wings much faster than other insects, and their one set of wings are rigid at the front and flexible at the rear, creating spinning masses of air for lift and propulsion.

RANGE: In small colonies in tiny places like vole holes across Europe and in a few small areas in the UK.

DIET: Nectar and pollen.

SIZE: 1–1.5cm long; smaller than average bumblebees.

STATUS: Britain's rarest bumblebees, they are classified Endangered on the UK Red List and listed on the UK Biodiversity Action Plan. Once common, they are now only found at seven locations in the UK and are declining in Europe, loss of habitat such as hedgerows being a major reason.

More than twelve factors such as air pollution, fungal diseases, parasites like the varroa mite, and loss of wild flower habitats are behind the decline of the world's bees. Bees are important as they are the major pollinators of human food crops.

# Bumblebee

The bumblebee,
with tiny wings,
so heavy from
her nose to sting,

it's been proved,
it's science fact,
she cannot fly –
and that is that.

So when you see
her buzzing by,
weighed down with
pollen on her thigh,

held up by whizzing
unseen wings -
she's not flying –
you're seeing things!

# Bipes tridactylus

There are three types of nocturnal, burrowing mole lizards, all pink and worm-like. One has five toes, one has four toes, and this one which has three toes. The strangest thing about them is that they only have front legs – no back legs! They move their front legs in an odd way, like the over-arm crawl used by a swimmer, and the rest of their long bodies with a sinuous snake-like writhe, which pushes them along.

RANGE: Only a few small areas of Mexico.

DIET: Worms and ants and other small creatures.

SIZE: 11–24cm.

STATUS: They are not listed as endangered by the IUCN Red List, but only live in small pockets in unprotected forests that may be lost to agriculture in the future. All three examples of this genus are listed on the Official Mexican Norm List of species considered at risk, as rare endemic species in need of special protection.

Recently both *Bipes canaliculatus* (four toes) and *Bipes tridactylus* appear to be experiencing serious declines in populations, apparently due to habitat alteration and the use of pesticides and fertilisers.

# Mole Lizard

Mole lizard's shape
has one long snag -
just two front legs
makes life a drag!

# Hemiceratoides hieroglyphica

Madagascan tear-drinking moths were discovered in 2006, when one was observed drinking the tears of a magpie robin. Many species of tear-drinking moths in Africa land on animals such as cattle or lions that can't brush them away. However these moths visit sleeping birds. Each moth uses its long, two- pronged, harpoon-like proboscis to open the birds' closed eyelids and sip tears. Tears contain protein and salt – salt is deficient in this area of Madagascar during the rainy season.

RANGE: Forests in Madagascar.

DIET: Tears.

SIZE: 2.5cm.

STATUS: Madagascan forests, where both magpie robins and robber moths live, are at risk from deforestation and habitat destruction, agricultural fires, hunting and over-collection of species from the wild. Illegal loggers are sending hardwoods like rosewood to Asia, Europe, the United States and China. The rainforests of the Atsinanana, on the east of the island, are on the UNESCO danger list.

Most of Madagascar's wildlife is so specialised it is at greater risk from climate change, which is also causing more devastating cyclones.

The United Kingdom is the second largest European Union importer of illegal timber.

# Madagascan Robber Moth

When robin ruffles
up her breast,
and shuts her eyes
at dark to rest,
while rain falls through
the forest night,
he takes to flight.

From powdered wings
no sound is heard,
he beats a path
to sleeping bird,
and settles on
her feathered head
with weightless tread.

While robin dreams
of where she flies,
safe roost in trees,
of song filled skies,
her forest full of
hopes and fears,
he steals her tears.

Then lifts to air;
so softly goes,
she never knows.

# Carinotetraodon travancoricus

Like all pufferfish, when threatened, Malabar pufferfish, or dwarf Indian pufferfish can puff themselves up with water until almost completely round. These little sharp-toothed fish are smooth, but many puffers have spines that are flat to their bodies when they are at rest, but which stick out at right angles when they are puffed up.

In addition to being able to scare predators away by appearing larger, and sometimes being a painful mouthful, most pufferfish contain tetrodotoxin. Tetrodotoxin is hundreds of times more poisonous than cyanide, and there is no known antidote. In Japan, some types of pufferfish are eaten as they are considered delicious. They have to be prepared very carefully so the dangerous parts of the fish are removed. Even so, some people die every year.

RANGE: Freshwater rivers in the Southern Ghats of India, in the coastal areas of Kerala and Southern Karnataka.

DIET: Zooplankton, various benthic crustaceans, molluscs and small, young crabs.

SIZE: 2.5cm

STATUS: These fish are classified by the IUCN Red List as Vulnerable – resulting from habitat modifications caused by deforestation and conversion of lands in agricultural areas, urbanisation, and over-harvesting for the pet trade. It is believed that in five years time, 30–40% of the population will have declined over a ten year period.

# Pufferfish

Those who think this little fish'll
make a very tasty dish'll
find as dinner starts to bristle,
that they've bitten on a thistle!

# *Pagodroma nivea*

Snow petrels are completely white birds with black eyes, bills and legs. Breeding further south than any other bird, they nest in crevices on cliff faces. The female leads the male in a fast, twisting, turning aerial chase, and if he wants a chance to mate with her, he has to keep up.

RANGE: Only in Antarctic waters, settling sometimes on ice floes and icebergs, but rarely landing on or in water.

DIET: Skimming the sea's surface they quickly scoop up small fish and krill, rarely diving.

SIZE: 30–40cm long.

STATUS: Snow petrels are not endangered. However of 131 species of petrel and albatross, 62% have been classified by the IUCN Red List as Extinct, Critically Endangered, Endangered, Vulnerable or Near Threatened. According to the World Wildlife Fund, causes include commercial fishing practices, loss of habitat, introduced predators, eating or becoming entangled in plastic waste, oil spills and climate change.

Dr. Simeon L Hill (Researcher, British Antarctic Survey), says, "Plausible forecasts suggest that 3ºC warming across the Antarctic could occur by the end of the century. This, in turn, would affect sea temperatures and sea ice cover, which could decrease by 33%, and likely impact the Antarctic krill population and the wider ecosystem in which it exists."

Although current predictions of these impacts are uncertain, this would not only affect Antarctic seabirds but seals, penguins, whales and the entire marine (Antarctic) ecosystem.

# Snow Petrels

On skies and seas
veiled white with light,
snow petrels weave
and wheel in flight,

they glide and skim
from high to low,
a falling flock
of feathered snow.

In courtship chases
pair by pair
they braid their paths
of freezing air,

birds of Antarctic
paradise,
the cliffs, the sea,
the snow, the ice.

# Giraffa camelopardalis ssp.peralta

Giraffes have nine sub-species, with different coat patterns, and within each sub-species, no two giraffes are alike. Their markings break up their body outlines and camouflage them very effectively.

For their size, giraffes have relatively small, very thick-walled hearts. These walls grow thicker as the giraffes' necks grow longer, as they need higher and higher blood pressure to pump blood with supercharged beats up to their brains.

Because of their height, they can see for many miles, and other mammals graze near them to take advantage of their ability to spot predators.

Giraffes can run for short distances at up to 48km/h.

RANGE: Sub-Saharan Africa – most common in East Africa and northern parts of Southern Africa.

DIET: Favourite foods are leaves from acacia, mimosa and apricot trees, which they pull off by winding with their 50cm prehensile tongues.

SIZE: The world's tallest terrestrial animal, measuring up to 5.5m high – the tallest male giraffe recorded was 6m high.

STATUS: This giraffe sub-species is classified by the IUCN Red List as Endangered, as it exists only in the wild and numbers fewer than 200 individuals, although under a targeted conservation programme, numbers are increasing. Threats to giraffes include habitat degradation and poaching.

# Giraffe

Ears                fan

fringed horns

and eyes

long        on top,

tongues,

which wind

wild apricot,

tall necks

that fall

in mobile

slopes,

designs

spun in

kaleido-

scopes,

all set

on stilts

so they

can rise

high up

to reach

acacia skies.

# Hyalinobatrachium pellucidum

These glass frogs are the precise colour of the leaves and stems on which they live. Their legs and arms are like opaque patterned glass, through which can be seen the colour of the surrounding leaves which helps camouflage them. It is possible to look right through the completely transparent skin on their bellies and see organs, including their beating hearts.

They are very delicate; when it rains they quickly retire or they might be knocked from their perch.

RANGE: Above streams in cloud forests on the Amazonian slopes of the Ecuadorian Andes. After breeding, when they lay their eggs on leaves over a stream, they disperse vertically and spend their time in the canopy.

DIET: Tiny insects.

SIZE: 1.5–2.5cm.

STATUS: These frogs are classified as Endangered on the IUCN Red List because of habitat destruction and degradation, primarily due to smallholder farming and logging. According to species expert Professor John D Lynch, (Curator of Amphibians, Universidad Nacional de Colombia), this sort of frog is relatively tolerant of habitat destruction, as long as gallery forest is left alongside their streams.

Almost half of the habitats suitable for this species have been deforested. It was last seen in 1979 when five specimens were collected from one forest site, which has since been destroyed.

# Glass Frog

With frosted glass hands glistening
on stems green as his green,

and eyes of golden amber,
polished to a gleam,

glass frog is transparently
safe to sit and dream,

camouflaged by clarity,
close by his forest stream.

# Ailuropoda melanoleuca

Giant pandas have an adapted wrist bone that acts like a thumb, which helps them to grasp stalks. This is useful, because as they have the inefficient digestive tract of a meat eater, and bamboo is nutritionally poor, they have to eat up to 38kg of it a day.

Bamboo plants take a long time to reach maturity, then they flower, seed and die, so pandas need to move to new areas periodically. Unfortunately their habitat is broken into 20 isolated patches that they cannot move between, so it is harder to find food. Isolation also causes problems with interbreeding and reduces their resistance to disease.

A panda baby is only 1/900 the size of its mother.

RANGE: China, where bamboo grows, between 500m and 3,000m above sea level.

DIET: They spend twelve hours a day eating bamboo, but they will also eat grass, fruit, insects, and small rodents.

SIZE: Up to 80cm, 1.5m long, with a 10–15cm tail.

STATUS: Giant pandas are classified as Endangered on the IUCN Red List. This is due to significant climate change, combined with thousands of years of cultivation of their lower habitats, expansion of agriculture upstream along river valleys (separating them into regions), and reliance on bamboo.

There are now only 1,600 giant pandas left in the wild.

# Panda

The black-eyed panda
eats bamboo,
he spends all day
with piles to chew,

it's all you see
a panda do-
but should snow hide
his stems from view,
too frozen stiff
to nibble through –

he'll snack on leaves
and bamboo rat –
I bet you didn't
expect that!

# *Somotochlora metallica*

Brilliant emerald dragonflies have apple-green eyes and bright green, metallic bodies with a bronze sheen.

Dragonflies can fly as fast as 56.3km/h, hover and fly backwards. They use 'unsteady aerodynamics', a different type of flight from that used by birds or aeroplanes. Their wings churn up air to create a whirling airflow that, despite their delicate frames, they can use without being thrown around.

Dragonfly flight is not yet perfectly understood, but scientists believe that the time lag between their front and rear wing flaps is very important for controlling their lift and propulsion.

RANGE: Europe and in fewer than ten locations in Great Britain.

DIET: Mosquitoes.

SIZE: 5.5cm long.

STATUS: Classified by the JNCC as Vulnerable on the Red List for British Odonata, as they occur in fewer than ten locations.

There are ten further species of resident British dragonflies classified as Near Threatened, Vulnerable or Endangered.

# Dragonfly

A glint of green,
a wink of wing,
whirl-winding air
while travelling,

knows the winds,
and knows the skies,
but no-one knows
how dragonflies.

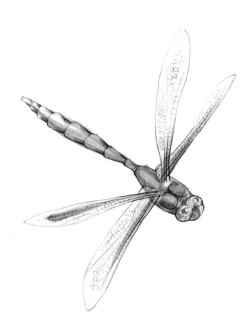

# *Stenorhynchus seticornis*

Arrowhead crabs have been seen hiding among and using anemones' stinging tentacles (which cannot harm them through their exoskeleton) as protection from predation. Their thin, articulated legs are up to three times the length of the unusual triangular carapace that gives them their name.

RANGE: The tropical Atlantic around Florida, the Bahamas, throughout the Caribbean and as far as South America. They hide in cracks and crevices on the sea floor during the day, at depths between 3m and 180m.

DIET: Small invertebrates, including featherdusters and bristleworms.

SIZE: 3–6cm.

STATUS: Arrowhead crabs are quite numerous and not listed as threatened, but they probably live in higher densities on corals than anywhere else. Corals are endangered everywhere Arrowhead crabs live, by climate change, coastal development and epidemic disease. Much of the crabs' prey also relies on coral.

Ocean acidification is also a major threat to corals. In 2010 the Center for Biological Diversity reported that, according to coral scientists, "Reefs are likely to be the first major planetary-scale ecosystem to collapse in the face of climate changes now in progress." The IUCN Red List classifies ten species of coral in this area as Near Threatened to Critically Endangered.

# Arrowhead Crab

All
acute
angles, it
spider stilts
across coral at
night, snatching
plankton in purple
pincers, attired arrowhead
to toes in pumpkin-striped pyjamas.

# Ardea insignis

White-bellied herons are known as 'gentle' giants as, although particularly large, they are shy and shun man. Jonathan Eames O.B.E. (Programme Manager, Birdlife International in Indochina) says that they live on the most remote and undisturbed rivers and soon disappear from rivers once humans make their presence known. Like many herons they are solitary feeders and their habits combined with their rarity suggest they are loners who live out their lives in remote, far-flung valleys.

RANGE: Once across the foothills of the Himalayas in Bhutan and northeast India and in the hills of Bangladesh and north Myanmar; now the few recent records come from five or six sites in Assam and Arunachal Pradesh, India, one or two sites in Bhutan, and parts of Myanmar.

DIET: Fish and other aquatic species. Herons swallow their food whole and have been known to choke on large fish.

SIZE: 1.27m tall.

STATUS: They are classified by the IUCN Red List as Critically Endangered due to loss of their habitat, and direct exploitation and disturbance. They are one of the most endangered birds in the world, possibly with only 50–249 mature individuals remaining.

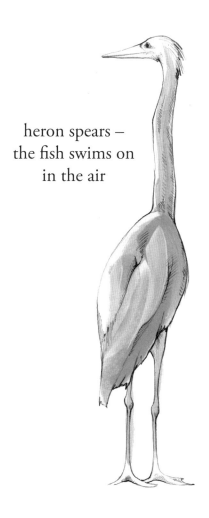

heron spears –
the fish swims on
in the air

# Rheobatrachus vitellinus

Eungella or northern gastric brooding frogs, were only discovered in 1984. Scientists watching the female frog witnessed her fully formed froglets leaving her mouth. They presumed she swallowed her fertilised eggs, but she may have guarded her egg mass and swallowed the tadpoles. It is thought her eggs and/or tadpoles excreted some form of enzyme that inhibited gastric digestion, as they proceeded to develop into fully formed froglets before being regurgitated.

Although the poem jokes about croaking, female frogs do not usually make a noise; it is the male frogs that croak.

RANGE: In streams in Eungella National Park, Queensland, Australia. Eungella is an Aboriginal name meaning 'Mountain of Clouds'.

DIET: Stream and stream-edge feeders, probably aquatic larvae of dragonflies, stoneflies and beetles.

SIZE: 5.5–8cm.

STATUS: Unfortunately, the last time these frogs were seen in the wild was in 1985, and they are now classified by the IUCN Red List as Extinct. The only other gastric brooding frogs (discovered in 1972, also in Australia) have not been seen since 1981 and are classified by the IUCN Red List as Extinct as well.

It is not known why Eungella gastric brooding frogs became extinct - but similar declines and disappearances elsewhere in the world were due to the chytridiomycosis fungus that is present in some rainforest streams at Eungella.

# The Northern Gastric Brooding Frog

The Eungella mother
swallows her spawn,
her stomach a womb
till her froglets are born,

waits weeks without food
until one by one,
her froglets emerge
leap-frogging her tongue.

During this childbirth
she can't croak a note,
as a matter of fact,
there's a frog in her throat...

# *Chioninia coctei*

The islands on which these giant Cape Verde skinks lived suffered widespread habitat destruction by humans, written about by Charles Darwin in 1832. In 1833 a group of convicts was stranded on one of the islands and the skinks were hunted for their meat and fat.

Live specimens were caught after this and some bought by zoos. Although some bred in captivity, sadly no live young ever hatched from their eggs.

RANGE: The islets of Branco and Raso in the Cape Verde Islands of the Atlantic Ocean, on rocks and in cavities and caves in the rock formations.

DIET: They were mainly herbivorous, possibly also eating small animals and birds' eggs.

SIZE: About 60cm, snout to tail.

STATUS: By 1940 these giant Cape Verde skinks had all disappeared, almost entirely due to human interference. Classified Extinct by the IUCN Red List.

# Skink

Skink.

Skink skinned.

Skin of skink.

Skink extinct.

# GLOSSARY

*Acidification* – a process where the seas are becoming more like an acid because they are absorbing carbon dioxide from the air.

*Arboreal* – living in trees.

*Biodiversity* – the number of different life forms in one place.

*Bromeliad* – a type of plant that grows on other plants and gets its food and water from the air and rain.

*Camouflage* – having colouring or movement or shape that makes a living thing hard to see in its habitat.

*Canopy* – the branches and leaves of the trees.

*Carapace* – the hard upper shell of an animal i.e. a beetle or turtle.

*Carnivorous* – meat eating.

*Crustacean* – an animal that lives in water and has no backbone, jointed limbs and an exoskeleton.

*Chemical contamination* – poison, usually from farming or industry, that is in or on food, water or land.

*Chytridiomycosis* – a fungus that is spreading across the world wiping out many species of amphibian.

*Climate change* – the overall warming of Earth, that will cause widespread changes to the balance of life, caused partly or mainly by human actions emitting carbon dioxide.

*Cryptic* – difficult to see, understand or work out.

*Cuticle* – a protective layer covering a living thing.

*Density* – how much of something is in a limited space.

*Ecosystem* – a community of animals and plants that rely on each other to live in a particular place.

*Feral* – wild animal, especially an escaped domesticated animal.

*Gallery forest* – forest in a strip alongside something like a river or projecting into treeless spaces.

*Genus* – a group of species exhibiting similar characteristics.

*Glycogen* – a substance stored in the liver and broken down into glucose when needed by the body.

*Habitat modification* – man-made alterations to habitat.

*Habitat degradation* – changing a habitat so that it is unable to feed, house, protect etc., the animals that used to live there.

*Hectare* – an area equal to 10,000 square metres.

*Honeydew* – a sweet liquid that aphids like greenfly produce by excretion.

*Invertebrates* – creatures without a backbone, like insects, slugs and snails.

*Krill* – numerous small shrimp-like crustaceans that are carried by sea-currents and that feed whales and other creatures.

*Nocturnal* – active at night.

*Oviduct* – a tube through which ova (eggs) pass to the womb or to the outside.

*Parasite* – an animal or plant that lives on or in another (its host) and gains its food from the host.

*Poisonous creatures* – have a substance that can injure or kill a living thing contained in part of their body, which is harmful when touched or eaten.

*Prehensile* – adapted so it can grasp or hold, especially by wrapping around an object.

*Proboscis* – the nose of a mammal or the long, sucking mouthparts of an insect.

*Propulsion* – the action of pushing forward.

*Reflex* – an automatic reaction to something that happens, e.g. a sneeze is a reflex to a tickle in the nose.

*Regurgitated* – brought back through the mouth.

*Revert* – return to a previous state or condition.

*Scats* – droppings.

*Species* – related organisms capable of breeding together.

*Specular* – having the reflective properties of a mirror.

*Toxic creatures* – produce a substance that is poisonous to other living creatures, delivered by a sting or fangs etc.

*Unregulated* – not protected by rules.

*UVB radiation* – strong, invisible ultraviolet rays from the sun that can damage cells.

# ORGANISATIONS MENTIONED IN THE TEXT

**The IUCN Red List of Threatened Species**™ - is widely recognised as the most comprehensive, objective global approach for evaluating the conservation status of plant and animal species.

*IUCN Red List categories referred to the text:*

*Extinct* –indicates there is no reasonable doubt that the last individual has died.

*Critically Endangered* – indicates an extremely high risk (more than 50%) of extinction in the wild.

*Endangered* – indicates a very high risk (more than 20%) of extinction in the wild.

Vulnerable – indicates that it is considered to be facing a very high risk (at least 10%) of extinction in the wild.

*Near Threatened* – indicates that a species is close to qualifying for, or is likely to qualify for, a threatened category in the near future.

**World Wildlife Fund** – for 50 years, WWF has been protecting the future of nature. The world's leading conservation organisation, WWF works in 100 countries and is supported close to 5 million members globally. WWF's unique way of working combines global reach with a foundation in science, involves action at every level from local to global, and ensures the delivery of innovative solutions that meet the needs of both people and nature.

**Joint Nature Conservation committee, JNCC** – is the public body that advises the UK Government and devolved administrations on UK-wide and international nature conservation.

**The UK Biodiversity Action Plan (UK BAP)** – was published in response to the Convention on Biological Diversity (CBD), which the UK signed up to in 1992 in Rio de Janeiro. The CBD called for the development and enforcement of national strategies and associated action plans to identify, conserve and protect existing biological diversity, and to enhance it wherever possible. UK BAP core information is kept on the JNCC website.

**United Nations Educational, Scientific and Cultural Organisation, UNESCO** – works to create the conditions for dialogue among civilizations, cultures and peoples, based upon respect for commonly shared values, to achieve global visions of sustainable development encompassing observance of human rights, mutual respect and the alleviation of poverty.

**Birdlife International** – is the world's largest global partnership of conservation organisations, and strives to conserve birds, their habitats and global biodiversity, working with people towards sustainability in the use of natural resources.

**Butterfly Conservation** – its mission is to conserve butterflies, moths and our environment, and to take practical action to conserve threatened butterflies and moths in the UK and elsewhere.

**Center for Biological Diversity** – believes that the welfare of human beings is deeply linked to nature – to the existence in our world of a vast diversity of wild animals and plants. They work to secure a future for all species, great and small, hovering on the brink of extinction through science, law and creative media.

**RSPB** – speaks out for birds and wildlife, tackling the problems that threaten our environment. Their work is focused on the species and habitats that are in the greatest danger.

# HOW MANY SPECIES ARE THREATENED?

This is hard to know for sure as large numbers of some species (e.g. insects) have not been assessed at all. Some data is available from the IUCN Red List. Here are just the species that are mentioned in this book that have been assessed enough to estimate a figure:

*41% of amphibians*
*13% of birds*
*33% of reef-forming corals*
*25% of mammals*

**Can you help?**

If you'd like to, these are things you can do:

The World Wildlife Fund, the RSPB, or any organisation working to save species and keep the Earth healthy, are always pleased to have new supporters. You can adopt an animal with the WWF – Hippos and Snow Leopards are two of the choices.

Have a look at labels on foods to see if they contain palm oil or anonymous 'vegetable fat'. Plantations of palm oil are the major reason for forest destruction. Particularly vulnerable are orangutans.

Many fish species are over-fished and some are obtained in ways that damage ecosystems – have a look on labels for 'caught by pole and line' and 'sustainable seafood'. The Marine Conservation Society lists supermarkets that sell sustainable seafood:
www.mcsuk.org/what_we_do/Fishing+for+our+future/Supermarket+survey/Supermarket+survey

You can buy food that is healthy for the environment – locally produced, organic, seasonal, vegetarian.

Changing to biodegradable and old-fashioned cleaning products such as soda crystals and bicarbonate of soda brings fewer harmful chemicals into your home and ultimately into the environment.

Check anything made of wood or paper, for a Forest Stewardship Council (FSC) logo. This makes sure wood comes from a responsibly managed forest. The UK is the second largest EU importer of illegal wood.

Save energy where you can to help save fuel and lower CO2 emissions, and save money. Turning lights etc off when not in use saves a lot of electricity and money. Turning heat down by one degree can save a considerable sum per year, and can also help you lose weight!

If you are buying a new item, see if there is an eco-friendly version.

Getting into a habit of keeping your own bags in your car to take shopping cuts down on plastic ones, they can take thousands of years to break down into tiny pieces which poison waterways, soil and the air. A lot of wildlife is harmed by plastic waste blowing off landfill.

If you are thinking of getting an exotic pet, ask if they have been bred in captivity – some creatures are taken from the wild.

There is a need for hedges, trees and areas of uncut grass, to provide food and protection for wildlife.

And finally, fun things to do – feed the birds, provide boxes for bats, nectar for butterflies, a home for a hedgehog, a frogitat, a bumblebee skep, a ladybird bug box – all available from the RSPB.

# REFERENCES

**Alaskan Wood Frog**

Reeves, Mari K. et al. (2008) *Road Proximity Increases Risk of Skeletal Abnormalities in Wood Frogs from National Refuges in Alaska.* Environ Health Perspect. 116(8): 1009–1014. [On-line] Accessed September 2011. Available from: www.ncbi.nlm.nih.gov/pmc/articles/PMC2516587/

Professor Brian Barnes, Director, Institute of Arctic Biology, University of Alaska Fairbanks. *Alaskan Wood Frogs,* emails to Liz Brownlee 4-6 October 2011.

**Ant**

*Butterfly Conservation.* [Online] Accessed June 2011. Available from: www.butterflyconservation.org/article/9/103/large_blue_butterflies_back_in_britain.html

Dr. George C. McGavin, Honorary Research Associate, Oxford University Museum of Nat. History, and Dept. of Zoology of Oxford University. *Notes and illustrations,ant,* email to Liz Brownlee, November 2011.

*Myrmica hirsuta* IUCN Red List [Online] Accessed May 2011. Available from: www.iucnredlist.org/apps/redlist/details/14232/0

**Arrowhead Crab**

Floyd E. Hayes, Professor of Biology, Department of Biology, Pacific Union College, Angwin, CA. *Stenorhynchus seticornis and poetry*, email to Liz Brownlee 18th October 2011.

*Stenorhynchus seticornis* Joshua Jones, James B Wood Ed. Marine invertebrates of Bermuda. [Online] Accessed October 2011. Available from: www.thecephalopodpage.org/MarineInvertebrateZoology/index.html

*Coral Conservation* Center for Biological Diversity [Online] Accessed September 2011. Available from: www.biologicaldiversity.org/campaigns/coral_conservation/index.html

**Bumblebee**

*Global Bee Colony Disorders and Other Threats to Insect Pollinators* [March 2011] United Nations Environment Programme [Online] Accessed September 2011. Available from: www.unep.org/Documents.Multilingual/Default.asp?DocumentID=664&ArticleID=6923

Professor Ismet Gursul, Professor of Aerospace Engineering, Dept, Mechanical Engineering, University of Bath. *Bees and poetry,* email to Liz Brownlee, September 1 2011.

*UK Biodiversity Action Plan Bees/wasps*, [2011] The National Archives. [Online] Accessed October 2011. Available from: webarchive.nationalarchives.gov.uk/20110303145213/http://ukbap.org.uk/UKPlans.aspx?ID=156

*Shrill carder bee (bombus sylvarum)* [Undated] Essex University Biodiversity Project. [Online] Accessed September 2011. Available from: www.essexbiodiversity.org.uk/Default.aspx?pageid=67

**Butterfly**

Richard Fox, Surveys Manager, Butterfly Conservation. *Butterflies and poetry,* email to Liz Brownlee October 2011.

*Butterfly Conservation* [Online] Accessed October 2011. Available from: www. butterfly-conservation.org/text/2044/40_years_of_butterfly_conservation.html

**Cave Racer Snake**

PRICE, Liz and Ya-Wei LI. (2007). The cave racer, *Orthriophis taeniurus. Cave and Karst Science* 34(3), pp129-134.

Liz Price, *Cave Racers,* emails to Liz Brownlee 12 March 2009, 13th March 2011.

**City Pigeon/Passenger Pigeon**

Dr. Karen Purcell, Project Leader, Celebrate Urban Birds, Cornell University Lab of Ornithology, NY. *Pigeons and poems,* email to Liz Brownlee 28th October 2011.

*Rock Dove,* RSPB [Online] Accessed May 2011. Available from: www.rspb.org.uk/ wildlife/birdguide/name/r/rockdove/index.aspx

*Ectopistes migratorius,* IUCN Red List, [Online] Accessed May 2011. Available from: www.iucnredlist.org/apps/redlist/details/106002553/0

*The Passenger Pigeon* Encyclopedia Smithsonian [Online] Accessed September 2011. Available from: www.si.edu/Encyclopedia_SI/nmnh/passpig.htm

**Crocodile**

Tom Dacey, Executive Officer, IUCN SSC Crocodile Specialist Group. *Philippine crocodiles and poetry,* email to Liz Brownlee 23 November 2011.

Dr. Jonathan E. M. Baillie, Conservation Programmes Director, Zoological Society of London. *Crocodiles and poetry,* email to Liz Brownlee 6 November 2011.

*Crocodylus mindorensis,* IUCN Red List. [Online] Accessed October 2011. Available from: www.iucnredlist.org/apps/redlist/details/5672/0

**Dormouse**

© *Natural England [2011]* Dormouse material is reproduced with the permission of Natural England, http://www.naturalengland.org.uk/copyright

*UK BAP priority terrestrial mammal species.* [Online] Joint Nature Conservation Committee (JNCC). Accessed September 2011. Available from: jncc.defra.gov.uk/ page-5170

**Dragonfly**

Professor Ismet Gursul, Professor of Aerospace Engineering, Dept, Mechanical Engineering, University of Bath. *Bees and poetry,* email to Liz Brownlee September 1, 2011.

Daguet, C.A., French, G.C. and Taylor, P. (2008). The Odonata Red Data List for Great Britain. *Species Status* **11**; 1-34. Joint Nature Conservation Committee, Peterborough. [Online] Available from: jncc.defra.gov.uk/page-4517 Accessed August 2011.

**European Eel**

*European Eel,* World Wildlife Fund, [Online] Accessed August 2011. Available from: wwf.panda.org/what_we_do/how_we_work/policy/conventions/cites/cites_cops/ cop14/agenda_species_2/eel_cites/

Dr. Steve Nicholls, Zoologist, Geologist and Entomologist, television documentary producer and director.

*Anguilla anguilla,* IUCN Red List, [Online] Accessed August 2011. Available from: www.iucnredlist.org/apps/redlist/details/60344/0

### Flying frog

Dr. Peter Paul van Dijk, Deputy Chair & Red List Focal Point, IUCN/SSC Tortoise & Freshwater Turtle Specialist Group, Director, Tortoise and Freshwater Turtle Conservation Program, Conservation International. *Rhacophorus reinwardtii and poetry,* email to Liz Brownlee 11 November 2011.

Robert Stuebing, Herpetolologist and Conservation Officer, *Malaysian Frogs and Poetry,* email to Liz Brownlee, December 2011.

*Rhacophorus reinwardtii,* IUCN Red List. [Online] Accessed October 2011. Available from: www.iucnredlist.org/apps/redlist/details/59017/0

### Gannet

Paul Nixen. Discovery Centre Manager of The Scottish Seabird Centre. 2007. *Gannets,* email to Liz Brownlee August 2007.

Dr. René Navarro, Animal Demography Unit, Department of Zoology, University of Cape Town, Rondebosch, South Africa. *Morus capensis and poetry,* email to Liz Brownlee 1 November 2011.

*Overlap between vulnerable top predators and fisheries in the Benguela upwelling system: implications for marine protected areas.* [2009] Marine Ecology Progress Series, contribution to the Theme Section 'Spatiotemporal dynamics of seabirds in the marine environment'. [Online] Accessed September 2011. Available from: *www.int-res.com/ articles/theme/m391p199.pdf*

*Morus capensis,* IUCN Red List. [Online] Accessed November 2011. Available from: www.iucnredlist.org/apps/redlist/details/106003653/0

### Giraffe

Professor Graham Mitchell, Emeritus Professor of Zoology and Physiology, University of Wyoming. *Giraffes and poetry,* emails to Liz Brownlee 14th, 16th, 19th September 2011.

*Giraffe, The Tall Blonde,* World Wildlife Fund. [Online] Accessed August 2011. Available from: wwf.panda.org/about_our_earth/teacher_resources/best_place_species/ current_top_10/giraffe.cfm

*Giraffa camelopardalis ssp. peralta,* IUCN Red List, [Online] Accessed September 2011. Available from: www.iucnredlist.org/apps/redlist/details/9194/0

### Glass Frog

John D. Lynch Associate Professor, Curator of Amphibians, Instituto de Ciencias Naturales of the Universidad Nacional de Colombia. *Hyalinobatrachium pellucidum and poetry,* email to Liz Brownlee 20th October 2011.

*Hyalinobatrachium pellucidum* IUCN Red List. [Online] Accessed September 2011. Available from: www.iucnredlist.org/apps/redlist/details/55028/0

### Heron

Jonathan Charles Eames O.B.E. Programme Manager, Birdlife International in

Indochina. *Ardea Insignis and poetry,* email to Liz Brownlee, November 1st 2011.

*Ardea Insignis* IUCN Red List [Online] Accessed September 2011. Available from: www.iucnredlist.org/apps/redlist/details/106003723/0

## Hippopotamus
Dr. Rebecca Lewison, Chair, IUCN/SSC Hippo Specialist Group, San Diego University, San Diego. *Hippopotamus amphibius and poetry,* email to Liz Brownlee 14th October 2011.

*Hippopotamus,* The giants who dance underwater, World Wildlife Fund. [Online] Available from: wwf.panda.org/about_our_earth/teacher_resources/best_place_ species/current_top_10/hippopotamus.cfm

*Hippopotamus amphibius* IUCN Red List [Online] Accessed May 2011. Available from: www.iucnredlist.org/apps/redlist/search

## Iguana
Townsend, Josiah H. et al. (2005) *First report of sporangia of a myxomycete (Physarum pusillum) on the body of a living animal, the lizard Corytophanes cristatus.* Mycologia. 97(2), pp. 346-348. [Online] Accessed September 2007. Available from: http://www. mycologia.org/cgi/content/full/97/2/346

Naskrecki, Piotr. (2005) *The Smaller Majority.* Massachusetts: Belknap Harvard, pp. 154-155.

Professor Robin Andrews, Dept. Biological Sciences, Virginia Tech, Blacksburg, Va, *Corytophanes cristatus,* email to Liz Brownlee 12 October 2011.

*UNESCO List of World Heritage in Danger,* [Online] Accessed August 2011. Available from: whc.unesco.org/en/danger/

## Leaf-Mimic Insect
Dr. George C. McGavin, Honorary Research Associate, Oxford University Museum of Nat. History, and Dept. of Zoology of Oxford University. *Typophyllum lunatum,* email to Liz Brownlee, 30 June 2011.

Dr. Sonja Wedmann Senckenberg Forschungsinstitut und Naturmuseum, Messel, Germany, *Antw. Leaf insects and poetry,* email to Liz Brownlee 28th October 2011.

Sonja Wedmann, *A brief review of the fossil history of plant masquerade by insects,* Article, Palaeontographica, Palaeontographica, Abt. B: Palaeobotany – Palaeophytology Article Vol. 283, Issues 4–6: 175–182 Stuttgart, September 2010. (Supplied by Sonja Wedmann.)

Marent, Thomas, with Morgan, Ben. (Undated) rainforest, a photographic journey. Dorling Kindersley, pp. 216-17.

## Leaf-Tailed Gecko
Glaw, F. & M. Vences (2007): A field guide to the amphibians and reptiles of Madagascar, third edition.- Vences & Glaw Verlag, 496 pp.

Dr. Frank Glaw, Zoologische Staatssammlung München, *Uroplatus henkeli and poetry,* email to Liz Brownlee October 2011.

## Madagascan Robber Moth
Dr. David C. Lees Researcher, Scientific Associate, Department of Entomology, Natural History Museum, Cromwell Road, London. *Hemiceratoides hieroglyphica and*

*poetry*, emails to Liz Brownlee 9ᵗʰ, 10th October 2011.

Roland Hilgartner, Mamisolo Raoilison, Willhelm Büttiker, David C Lees and Harald W. Krenn. *Malagasy birds as hosts for eye-frequenting moths.* Biol. Lett. (2007) 3, 117–120 DOI:10.1098/rsbl.2006.0581 [Online] 4 January 2007. (Supplied by David C Lees.)

*UNESCO List of World Heritage in Danger* [Online] Accessed August 2011. Available from: whc.unesco.org/en/danger/

## Mirror Beetle

Donald B Thomas, WWF Research Entomologist, USDA Agrigultural Research Service, expert scarabaeidae beetle diversity. *Chrysina strasseni,* email to Liz Brownlee 12ᵗʰ October 2011.

Donald B. Thomas, Ainsley Seago, and David C. Robacker. Reflections On Golden Scarabs. American Entomologist [Online] [Winter 2007] Accessed May 2011. Available from: www.entsoc.org/PDF/Pubs/Periodicals/AE/AE-2007/.../Thomas.pdf

*UNESCO List of World Heritage in Danger* [Online] Accessed August 2011. Available from: whc.unesco.org/en/danger/

## Mole Lizard

Carl J Franklin, Biological Curator, Amphibian and Reptile Diversity Research Center, University of Texas at Arlington Dept. of Biology. *Bipes and poetry,* email to Liz Brownlee 8ᵗʰ November 2011.

*CONSERVATION OF BIODIVERSITY in MÉXICO: ECOREGIONS, SITES AND CONSERVATION TARGETS.* The Nature Conservancy Mexico Div. Conservation Science and Stewardship. Sept. 2000. Juan E. Bezaury Creel et al. [Online] Accessed August 2011. Available from: *www.protectedareas.info/upload/.../ecoregionalplan-mexico.pdf*

## Northern Gastric Brooding Frog

*Rheobatrachus vitellinus* – Northern Gastric Brooding Frog, Eungella Gastric Brooding Frog, Australian Government, Dept. of Sustainability, Environment, Water, Population and Communities, (2011) Biodiversity, Species Profile and Threats Database. [Online] Accessed November 2011. Available from: http://www.environment.gov.au/sprat.

Professor Michael Mahoney, School of Environmental and Life Sciences, Faculty of Science and Information Technology, University of Newcastle, Callaghan, Australia. *Rheobatrachus vitellinus and poetry,* email to Liz Brownlee 17-18ᵗʰ October 2011.

*Rheobatrachus vitellinus* IUCN Red List [Online] Accessed August 2011. Available from: www.iucnredlist.org/apps/redlist/details/19476/0

## Orang-utan

Emmons, L.H. 1995. Mammals of Rainforest Canopies. Pp. 199-222 in Lowman Margaret D, Nadkarni (eds.), *Forest Canopies*, San Diego: Academic Press. [On-line] Accessed June 2007. Available from: http://books.google.com/books?id=F471I0uJv-8C&dq=lowman+rinker+forest+canopies&printsec=frontcover&source=web&ots=GStA5KnhPH&sig=ppcMvPgHPRN22hNf9sCrmE3uRWs#PPA260,M1

Louise Emmens, Adjunct Scientist, Division of Mammals, Smithsonian Institution.

*Pongo pygmaeus*, emails to Liz Brownlee, November 2007, 29th July 2011.

*Orangutans*, World Wildlife Fund. [Online] Accessed June 2011. Available from: wwf.panda.org/what_we_do/endangered_species/great_apes/orangutans/

*Pongo pygmaeus*, IUCN Red List. [Online] Accessed April 2011. Available from: www. iucnredlist.org/apps/redlist/details/17975/0

*Pongo abelii*, IUCN Red List. [Online] Accessed April 2011. Available from: www. iucnredlist.org/apps/redlist/details/39780/0

Carter, M. L., Pontzer, H., Wrangham, R. W. and Peterhans, J. K. (2008), Skeletal pathology in *Pan troglodytes schweinfurthii* in Kibale National Park, Uganda. American Journal of Physical Anthropology, 135: 389–403. doi: 10.1002/ajpa.20758

**Orb Spider**

Matjaž Kuntner, Evolutionary Zoology lab, Jovan Hadži, Institute of Biology, Scientific Research Centre of the Slovenian Academy of Sciences and Arts, Ljubljana, Slovenia. *Nephila komaci and poetry*, email to Liz Brownlee 14 October 2011.

Mercier, Claire. Undated. *Vibration transmission characteristics of silk produced by the British cribellate spider Amaurobius similis*. [On-line] Accessed October 2011. Available from: www.fbs.leeds.ac.uk/students/ejournal/Biolog-e/uploads/clairemercier.pdf

Dr. George C. McGavin, Honorary Research Associate at Oxford University Museum of Natural History and Dept. Zoology at Oxford University. *Orb spider*, email Liz Brownlee 2009.

**Origami Frog**

Behler, John L, Behler Deborah A. (2005) *Frogs, a Chorus of Colors*. New York: Sterling Publishing Co., Inc., p. 38.

Martin Pickersgill, Assessor African Amphibians IUCN, *Afrixalus delicatus*, email Liz Brownlee 7 November 2011.

*Afrixalus delicatus* IUCN Red List, [Online] Accessed July 2011. Available from: www.iucnredlist.org/apps/redlist/details/56059/0

**Panda**

*Panda*, facts and species fact sheet. World Wildlife Fund. [Online] Accessed September 2011. Available from:wwf.panda.org/what_we_do/endangered_species/giant_panda/

*Ailuropoda melanoleuca*, IUCN Red List. [Online] Accessed September 2011. Available from: www.iucnredlist.org/apps/redlist/details/712/0

**Poison Dart Frog**

Professor Molly Cummings, Associate Professor Section of Integrative Biology, University of Texas, Austin. *Oophaga pumilio*, email to Liz Brownlee 12 October 2011.

Dr. Martine Maan, University of Groningen, CBN Behavioural Biology, Nijenborgh 7 9747, Groningen. *Oophaga pumilio*, email to Liz Brownlee 13th October 2011.

Saporito, R.A., Donnelly, M.A., Spande, T.F., and Garraffo, H.M. (2011) A review of chemical ecology in poison frogs. *Chemoecology*, [Online] Sept. 9. Accessed October 2011. Available from: sites.google.com/site/ralphsaporito/publications DOI 10.1007/ s00049-011-0088-0

Mattison, Chris. (2011) *Frogs and Toads.* Natural History Museum, pp 60.

*Phyllobates terribilis* IUCN Red List, [Online] Accessed September 2011. Available from: www.iucnredlist.org/apps/redlist/details/55264/0

**Polkadot Frog**

Professor Molly Cummings, Associate Professor Section of Integrative Biology, University of Texas, Austin. *Oophaga pumilio*, email to Liz Brownlee 13 October 2011.

Dr. Martine Maan, University of Groningen, CBN Behavioural Biology Nijenborgh 7 9747 Groningen *Oophaga pumilio*, email to Liz Brownlee 13th October 2011.

Mattison, Chris. (2011) *Frogs and Toads.* Natural History Museum, pp 113.

*Oophaga arborea* IUCN Red List. [Online] Accessed October 2011. Available from: www.iucnredlist.org/apps/redlist/details/55173/0

**Pufferfish**

Dr. Neelesh Dahanukar IISER Fellow, Indian Institute of Science Education and Research, Pune, India. *Carinotetraodon travancoricus,* emails to Liz Brownlee 13-17th October 2011.

*Carinotetraodon travancoricus,* IUCN Red List. [Online] Accessed September 2011. Available from: www.iucnredlist.org/apps/redlist/details/166591/0

**Pygmy Shrew**

Don E Wilson, Curator Emeritus, Division of Mammals, Smithsonian Institution, Washington, DC. *Pygmy shrews and poetry,* email to Liz Brownlee 1 November 2011.

*Channa. N. B. Bambaradeniya,* (2006) The Fauna of Sri Lanka: Status of Taxonomy, Research and Conservation. [Online] Accessed July 2011. Available from: *www.iucn. org/dbtw-wpd/edocs/2006-030.pdf*

*Suncus fellowesgordoni,* IUCN Red List. [Online] Accessed July 2011. Available from: www.iucnredlist.org/apps/redlist/details/21143/0

**Rattlesnake**

Dr. Christopher L. Jenkins, Chief Executive Officer & Executive Director, The Orianne Society, South Clayton, GA. *Rattlesnakes and poetry,* email to Liz Brownlee 29th October 2011.

*Crotalus unicolor* IUCN Red List. [Online] Accessed July 2011. Available from: www.iucnredlist.org/apps/redlist/details/5685/0

**Red-Breasted Geese**

Malte Andersson, Profesor Emeritus, Animal Ecology, Dept. Zoology, University of Gothenburg. *Geese, formation flying and poetry,* email to Liz Brownlee 10 November 2011.

*Evidence and Implications of Dangerous Climate Change in the Arctic* [2005) World Wildlife Fund [Online] Accessed October 2011. Available from: www.wwf.org.uk/search_results.cfm?searchText=Red-breasted+geese

*Branta ruficollis* IUCN Red List. [Online] Accessed August 2011. Available from: www.iucnredlist.org/apps/redlist/details/100600387/0

**Red-Crowned Crane**

Simba Chan (Mr) Senior Conservation Officer BirdLife International Asia Division. *Grus japonensis and poetry,* email to Liz Brownlee 14th October 2011.

Scott Swengel, Independent zoologist and former Curator of Birds at the International Crane Foundation. *Grus japonensis and poetry,* email to Liz Brownlee 1 November 2011.

Ellis, David H et al. (1998/5//) *A sociogram for the cranes of the world.* Jour, Behavioural Processes. 43: 2: 125: 151 [Online] Available from: http://www.sciencedirect.com/science/article/pii/S0376635798000084 doi: 10.1016/S0376-6357(98)00008-4 Accessed August 2011.

*Grus japonensis* IUCN Red List [Online] Accessed August 2011. Available from: www.iucnredlist.org/apps/redlist/details/106002798/0

Masatomi, H. 1994. *Structure and function of crane dance.* The Future of Cranes and Wetlands: 146-148.

**Sand Cat**

Kristin Nowell, Director CAT, Cat Action Treasury, IUCN Cats Red List Focal Point. *Sand cats, Snow leopards and poetry,* email to Liz Brownlee 27th October 2011.

*Felis margarita,* IUCN Red List, [Online] Accessed March 2010. Available from: www.iucnredlist.org/apps/redlist/details/8541/0

**Sea Star**

Dr. Tim O Hara, Senior Curator of Marine Invertebrates, Museum Victoria, Australia. *Sea stars and poetry,* email to Liz Brownlee November 11, 2011.

Dr. Christopher Mah, Researcher Dept Invertebrate Zoology, Smithsonian Institution. *Sea stars and poetry,* email to Liz Brownlee 7 October 2011.

*Echinoblog* Sea Stars [Online] Accessed May 2010. Available from: echinoblog.blogspot.com

Dr. Julian (Tony) Koslow, Director, Scripps CalCOFI program, Scripps Institution of Oceanography, University of California. *Sea stars and poetry,* email to Liz Brownlee 27th October 2011.

Professor Dan Laffoley, IUCN, Senior Advisor, Marine Science and Conservation Global Marine and Polar Programme. *Sea stars and poetry,* email to Liz Brownlee 26th October 2011.

Professor Callum Roberts, Marine Conservation Biologist, Environment Dept. York University. *Sea stars and poetry,* email to Liz Brownlee 26th October 2011.

**Skink**

Dr. Franco Andreone, Curator at Zoology Dept, Museo Regionale di Scienze Naturali, Torino, Italy. *Macroscincus (Chioninia) coctei and poetry,* email to Liz Brownlee 12 October 2011.

*Macroscincus (Chioninia) coctei,* IUCN Red List [Online] Accessed April 2011. Available from: www.iucnredlist.org/apps/redlist/details/12644/0

**Skylark**

*Skylark,* RSPB [Online] Accessed August 2011. Available from: www.rspb.org.uk/wildlife/birdguide/name/s/skylark/index.aspx

*UK Biodiversity Action Plan.* [Online] Accessed August 2011. Available from: *jncc. defra.gov.uk*

**Snow Leopard**

*Snow Leopard,* World Wildlife Fund, [Online] Accessed August 2011. Available from: wwf.panda.org/what_we_do/endangered_species/snow_leopard/

*Panthera uncia* IUCN Red List. [Online] Accessed August 2011. Available from: www.iucnredlist.org/apps/redlist/details/22732/0

Royal Horticultural Society, *Query about mountain roses,* email to Liz Brownlee 18th September 2011.

**Snow Petrel**

Dr. Ross Wanless, Birdlife Conservation International. *Pagodroma nivea and poetry,* email to Liz Brownlee 14 Oct 2011.

Dr. Simeon L Hill, British Antarctic Survey, Cambridge. *Artistnwritersquery via BAS website,* email to Liz Brownlee 31 October 2011.

Dr. Richard A Phillips, British Antarctic Survey. *Artistnwritersquery via BAS website,* email to Liz Brownlee 31 October 2011.

**Torrent Frog**

Professor Albert S Feng, Professor Emeritus of Molecular and Integrative Physiology, Neuroscience, Bioengineering, and Biophysics, Beckman Institute, Illinois. *Odorrona tormota,* email to Liz Brownlee, 6th October 2011.

*Odorrana tormota,* Female Frog's Ultrasonic Way of Asking for Sex. [Online] e! Science News Sunday, May 11, 2008 - 21:56 in Biology & Nature Accessed September 2011. Available from: esciencenews.com/sources/scientific.blogging/2008/05/11/odorrana. tormota.female.frogs.ultrasonic.way.of.asking.for.sex

*Odorrana tormota,* IUCN Red List. [Online] Accessed September 2011. Available from: www.iucnredlist.org/apps/redlist/details/58226/0

**Vogelkop Bowerbird**

Dr. Gerald Borgia Department of Biology University of Maryland College Park, MD. *Amblyornis inornatus and poetry,* email to Liz Brownlee, 17th October, 2011.

*New Guinea, Safeguarding the natural world – forests.* World Wildlife Fund [Online] Accessed September 2011. Available from: www.wwf.org.uk/what_ we_do/safeguarding_the_natural_world/forests/forest_work/new_guinea_ forest/?pc=AJB004002

**Wren**

Alvaro Jaramillo, Senior Biologist, San Francisco Bay Bird Observatory. *Cobb's wren and poetry,* email to Liz Brownlee 24th October 2011.

*Cobb's Wren,* Falklands.net Regional Member of the International Penguin Conservation Group (IPCWG). [Online] Accessed October 2011. Available from: www.falklands.net/BirdGuideCobbsWren.shtml

*Troglodytes cobbi,* IUCN Red List. [Online] Accessed September 2011. Available from: www.iucnredlist.org/apps/redlist/details/106009769/0

**ROSE SANDERSON** Based in Bristol, UK, Rose completed her BA (hons) in Illustration in 2003. Since then she has exhibited in a number of locations throughout the world. Inspired by nature, her delicate yet expressive paintings aim to expose the beauty in all that is part of life's fragile cycle. www.rosesanderson.com